Against the Odds

Contents

Picking Teams

When we pick teams in the playground,
Whatever the game might be,
There's always somebody left till last
And usually it's me.

I stand there looking hopeful
And tapping myself on the chest,
But the captains pick the others first,
Starting, of course, with the best.

Maybe if teams were sometimes picked
Starting with the worst,
Once in his life a boy like me
Could end up being first!

Alan Ahlberg

Everyone hates the feeling of not being good enough. Everyone wants to succeed. This story is about Olga da Polga, a guinea pig who is entered in a pet show. She doesn't even know what the competition is about, but she still wants to do well. Why is she so sure she will win?

Olga Wins a Prize

One day, something unusual happened to Olga da Polga, the guinea pig. Instead of being taken back home in the usual fashion, she found herself being carried into the big house where the Sawdust family lived.

She was taken through the kitchen, along a passage, and into a big room, where she was placed on top of a thing called a "table". It was a large area of very slippery wood high off the ground, with NO SIDES WHATSOEVER.

Olga knew all this because Karen Sawdust, who had been carrying her, explained matters as they went along.

She sat very still, hardly daring to move, while everyone gathered round and began prodding, poking, staring and even – biggest indignity of all – TURNING HER UPSIDE DOWN!

Olga was most upset. "How would they like it", she thought, "if someone came along and turned them upside down? It's not nice. It's not nice at all." And she gave a passing nip to the hand which happened to be holding her.

After that she felt a trifle better.

It wasn't really a hard nip, but hard enough to leave a mark and to show exactly how she felt about the matter.

Then something even worse happened. A large object like a . . . like a . . . Olga tried hard to think just what it did remind her of, descended on her. A hedgehog! That was it. The object looked just like a hedgehog.

For a moment Olga thought she was going to be attacked, she wriggled and struggled to avoid this latest outrage to her person.

"Come along, Olga," said Karen Sawdust firmly, as she tried to hold her still, "If you're

going to be entered for a show you must have your fur brushed. You want to look your best don't you?"

Olga felt her heart miss a beat. "Entered for a show! Me? In a show?"

She'd heard about SHOWS from some of the guinea-pigs who visited her on occasions. Some of her friends even knew other guinea-pigs who had been in such things. One of them, Charles, boasted of a cousin several times removed who'd actually won a prize. But as no one had ever met the animal in question this was taken with a pinch of oats.

It made a difference knowing the reason, and Olga lay back and let the brush ruffle through her fur. Really, it was quite a nice feeling. Tingling, but most pleasant, and very good for itches.

"Just wait until I see them next," she breathed, thinking of all her friends. "Just wait until I tell them!"

She went back to her house later that evening looking unusually spruce and well-groomed and with a definite air about her, for it never crossed Olga's mind for a second that she wouldn't win a prize.

It wasn't that she was particularly vain, or boastful, or even that she thought a lot of herself. It simply didn't cross her mind.

From the moment she heard she was going in for a show Olga thought of nothing else.

And there was so much to do. If she wasn't worrying about where she was going to put her prize – for it might turn out to be a large one – she was worrying over her diet.

"I must build myself up," she kept saying. "I must eat as much as possible. It's no good looking skinny."

And eat she did. Grass, dandelions, groundsel, clover, paper, cornflakes – Olga was very keen on cornflakes, though she usually only got them on Sundays – oats, anything and everything that came within range of her mouth disappeared in a trice.

And every day her fur was brushed until it shone like the table top itself.

At last the great day came. Olga was up bright and early and after a final going-over with the brush and comb and a wash of her paws she was on her way.

"Of course, the trouble with shows," said Olga once she was settled next to a bored-looking rabbit in a neighbouring hutch, "is all the waiting around. I mean they might just as well hand out the prize straightaway and let everyone else go home. It would save all this mucking about."

Really it was quite true. For every one person who came and stared at her and then went away again there were a hundred. Some made notes on pieces of paper. Others just talked. Then she was taken out of her box and made to stand on some things called "scales". Goodness only knew why.

After which there was a lot of hemming and haw-
ing and more chatter and note-taking.

"Talk! Talk! Talk!" muttered Olga. "Why on
earth don't they get on with it?"

"You should know by now," said the rabbit,
who was also getting a bit restive, "that human
beings always talk. They can't even dig a hole in
the ground without discussing it first. Not like us
rabbits."

But at last the big moment came. The moment Olga had been waiting for. In fact, she was so quietly confident about the outcome of the contest she hardly batted an eyelid when one of the judges stepped forward and pinned something on her travelling hutch.

"Such a nice, intelligent man," she thought, as everyone applauded. "Not that he had much choice, of course, but he did it very nicely."

When she was being put back in her own house and caught sight of a blue rosette on the side of her travelling hutch she grew even more lyrical.

"A rosette!" she cried. "A rosette! Wheeeeee! It's the story of the prince all over again." And she looked round at herself to see if she had grown any more rosettes of her own.

She felt quite disappointed when she found she
hadn't. Perhaps they took time to take root.

It wasn't until she caught something in the tone
of Karen Sawdust's voice as she placed her carefully back in the straw that a slight feeling of doubt
crossed Olga's mind.

"Fancy!" chuckled Karen. "I've heard of guinea-
pigs winning first prize for having the longest fur.
I've heard of them winning first prize for having
the smoothest and I've even seen awards for the
longest whiskers ... but yours ..." The voice
dissolved into gales of laughter as the door closed.
"It just serves you right for being so greedy!"

Olga sat for a while lost in thought. What could
she have meant? Me ... greedy? What sort of
prize had she won?

She squinted through the window at the rosette still pinned to the travelling hutch and at the piece of card just below it.

Reading upside down wasn't Olga's strong point and although she had once, ages ago it now seemed, managed to spell out her name when there had been all the fuss about what to call her, new words were much more difficult and the writing on the card took a lot longer.

But then, FIRST PRIZE TO OLGA DA POLGA FOR BEING THE FATTEST GUINEA-PIG IN THE SHOW is a lot to get on to a very small card, especially when the reader is so indignant she can hardly believe her own eyes.

On the other hand, if it did nothing else it certainly cured Olga of being greedy. At least for the time being!

Michael Bond

Olga da Polga prepared for her competition by eating a lot, but eating is not usually the way to win a competition.

Most people know how to run, jump and throw things. These are the skills that are tested in athletics. But, to be successful in athletics isn't easy. You need talent, strength, and above all the will-power to go on trying, day after day, event after event, whether you win or lose.

Daley Thompson knew he would have to work very hard if he really wanted to succeed in athletics.

Will - power

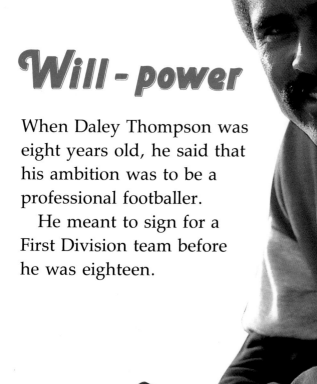

When Daley Thompson was eight years old, he said that his ambition was to be a professional footballer.

He meant to sign for a First Division team before he was eighteen.

There was nothing unusual about that. Hundreds of people want to be footballers. What was unusual was the hard work Daley put into it. He went training every morning before school, every dinner-time and every afternoon. He played evening and weekend matches, sometimes as many as seven in a week. People said, "That boy's football mad." But they always added, "Mind you, he's very good at it."

When Daley was sixteen, his headmaster sent him for track training at a local athletics club, the Haywards Heath Harriers. The idea was to improve his sprinting, to make him the fastest runner on the football field. But as soon as Daley began athletics training, he fell in love with the sport. He decided to turn his ambition from football to athletics.

At first, Daley couldn't decide which event to specialise in. He was good at sprinting, distance-running, hurdling, high-jumping and long-jumping. Then his coach had a brainwave. "Try the decathlon," he said. "That will use all your skills."

Decathlon means "ten contests". It has ten events, each testing a different skill. A decathlon is spread over two days.

Day 1: 100 metres dash; long jump; shot put; high jump; 400 metres race.

Day 2: 110 metres hurdles; discus; pole vault; javelin; 1500 metres race.

You don't have to be a champion at all ten events. You win points for each of them according to your placing, and the winner is the athlete with most points at the end of all ten events.

The most important things a decathlete needs are concentration and a wide range of skills. This was ideal for Daley. He kept on practising the events he was good at, like hurdling and high-jump, and worked really hard to improve the others. He hated the pole vault especially, and often fell – so he made that the event he trained for hardest of all.

In 1975, aged 17, Daley won the Welsh Open decathlon championship. From then on, he started training for the Olympic Games. He began each day with gym-work and road-running, to build up his strength. He spent two or three hours each day at the stadium, practising each of his ten events. And he entered every competition he could, from local matches to big internationals, where he could test himself against other decathletes, and try the opposition.

At the 1976 Olympics, Daley was a respected but not brilliant performer. His big chance came four years later, at the 1980 Moscow Olympic Games. He had been selected for Great Britain, and lined up for the first day of the decathlon with twenty-one competitors from countries across the world. That was one of the greatest days of Daley's life. He won the 100 metres, the long jump

and the 400 metres, and by the end of the day he had scored the huge total of 4542 points, 264 ahead of his nearest rival.

The next day was cold and rainy. The discus and the pole for the pole vault would be slippery, and on his way to the stadium Daley slipped and fell, so that he felt bruised and shaken. It was determination that pulled him through. He didn't try to break records in any of the second day's events. His aim was just to get through them, with good enough results to win the points he needed. He ended up with a total of 8495 points, and stood anxiously waiting while the computer added up the points of his nearest rival. 8331. Daley had won! He was the Olympic champion, the winner of the gold medal, the finest decathlete in the world.

Four years later, Daley repeated his success at the 1984 Los Angeles Olympic Games. And the day after his victory, instead of relaxing or retiring, he started training once more. He meant to win again, at the next Olympic Games. He wanted to be the only person in the world ever to win three decathlon gold medals in three Olympic Games. To most people, that would be an impossible ambition. But Daley Thompson, with his will to win and the hard work he puts in, hour after hour, day after day, is just the man to do it.

Kenneth McLeish

"Hodja" is a title given by Muslims to someone who has made the journey to the holy city of Mecca and then returned home. A Hodja is thought to be a wise and holy man.

Daley Thompson accepted his defeats as part of his training. The Hodja in this story has no intention of accepting defeat even when his friends seem to have won.

But if everybody cheats, who has really won?

Fair Play

Once upon a time, during a very cold winter, the Hodja's friends offered to make a bet with him.

"If you stand all night on the village square, and do not move, and do not try to warm yourself in any way, we shall give you a good dinner. If you fail, you must give us one."

"All right," said the Hodja.

All that night he stood motionless in the snow and frost. When morning came he rushed triumphantly up to his friends. "I have won the bet!" he shouted.

"Tell us what happened," they replied.

"I stood still all night on the village square. I nearly froze, but I didn't move."

"Did anything happen?"

"Well, at about midnight I did see a candle burning in a window about 3 miles away."

"Then you've lost the bet!" cried his friends. "You warmed yourself by the flame of the candle, and you lost the bet."

They would not listen to him any more, so the Hodja was forced to invite them to his house for dinner.

That night the friends all arrived in a good mood and waited for their dinner. They waited and waited. After about four hours they went to see if the Hodja really was cooking them dinner. In the kitchen they saw a huge cauldron hanging over the tiny flame of a candle. "Hodja!" they exclaimed. "What on earth is going on? How can you expect such a small flame to boil such a large pot?"

"You convinced me it was possible," laughed the Hodja. "If I was kept warm by a candle three miles away, surely the same flame will boil a pot only three inches away!"

Kathy Leyshon

The Hodja used his wits so that he would not lose. That is what you must do if you are competing against someone much stronger than you. You must use your brains to win.

This is what Polly does. The wolf is stronger than Polly and he tries to be crafty. But is he as clever as Polly?

Monday's Child

Polly was sitting in the garden making a daisy chain. She had grown her right thumb nail especially long on purpose to be able to do this. For the last two weeks she had said to her mother, "Please don't cut the nail on that thumb, I need it long." And her mother obligingly hadn't. Now it was beautifully long and only a little black. Polly slit up fat pink stalk after fat pink stalk. The daisy chain grew longer and longer.

As she worked, Polly talked to herself. It was half talking, half singing.

"Monday's child is fair of face," she said. "Tuesday's child is full of grace. Wednesday's child – "

"Is good to fry," interrupted the wolf. He was looking hungrily over the garden wall.

"That's not right," said Polly indignantly. "It's Wednesday's child is full of woe, Thursday's child has far to go. There's nothing about frying in it at all."

"There's nothing about woe, or going far in the poem I know," protested the wolf. "What would be the use of that?"

"The use?" Polly repeated. "It isn't meant to be useful, exactly. It's just to tell you what children are like when they're born on which days."

"Which days?" the wolf asked, puzzled.

"Well, any day, then."

"But which is a Which Day?"

"Oh dear," said Polly. "Perhaps I didn't explain very well. Look, Wolf! If you're born on a Monday you'll be fair of face, because that is what the poem says. And if you're born on a Tuesday you'll be full of grace. See?"

"I'd rather be full of food," the wolf murmured, "I don't think grace sounds very satisfying."

"And if you're born on a Wednesday you'll be full of woe," said Polly, taking no notice of the interruption.

"Worse than grace," the wolf said. "But my poem's quite different. My poem says that Wednesday's child is good to fry. That's much more useful than knowing that it's full of woe. What good does it do anyone to know that? My poem is a useful poem."

"Is it all about frying?" Polly asked.

The wolf thought for a moment.

"No," he said presently. "None of the rest of it is about frying. But it's good. It tells you the sort of thing you want to know. Useful information."

"Is it all about cooking?" Polly asked severely.

"Well, yes, most of it. But it's about children too," the wolf said eagerly.

"That's disgusting," said Polly.

"It isn't, it's most interesting. And instructive. For instance, I can probably guess what day of the week you were born on, Polly."

"What day?"

The wolf looked at Polly carefully. Then he looked up at the sky and seemed to be repeating something silently to himself.

"Either a Monday or a Friday," he said at last.

"It was a Monday," Polly admitted. "But you could have guessed that from my poem."

"What does yours say?" the wolf asked.

"Monday's child is fair of face, Tuesday's child is full of grace, and I am fair, in the hair anyway," Polly said.

"Go on. Say the whole poem."

Polly said:

"Monday's child is fair of face,
Tuesday's child is full of grace.
Wednesday's child is full of woe,
Thursday's child has far to go.
Friday's child is loving and giving,
Saturday's child works hard for its living.
But the child that is born on the Sabbath day
Is bonny and blithe and good and gay."

"Pooh," cried the wolf. "What a namby-pamby poem! There isn't a single thing I'd want to know about a child in the whole thing. And, anyway, most of it you could see with half an eye directly you met the child."

"You couldn't see that it had far to go," Polly argued.

"No," the wolf agreed. "That's the best line certainly. But it depends how far it had to go, doesn't it? I mean if it had gone a long, long way from home you might be able just to snap it up without any fuss. But then it might be tough from taking so much exercise. Not really much help."

"It isn't meant to be much help in the way you mean," said Polly.

"And it isn't what I call a poem, either," the wolf added.

"Why?" asked Polly. "It rhymes, doesn't it?"

"Oh, rhymes," said the wolf scornfully. "Yes, if that's all you want. It jingles along if that satisfies you. No. I meant it doesn't make you go all funny inside like real poetry does. It doesn't bring tears to your eyes and make you feel you understand life for the first time, like proper poetry."

"Is the poem you know proper poetry?" Polly asked suspiciously.

"Certainly it is," the wolf said indignantly. "I'll say it to you and then you'll see.

Monday's child is fairly tough,
Tuesday's child is tender enough,
Wednesday's child is good to fry,
Thursday's child is best in pie.
Friday's child makes good meat roll,
Saturday's child is casserole.
But the child that is born on the Sabbath day,
Is delicious when eaten in any way.

Now you can't hear that without having some pretty terrific feelings, can you?"

The wolf clasped his paws over his stomach and looked longingly at Polly.

"It gives me a queer tingling feeling in my inside," he went on. "Like a sort of beautiful, hungry pain. As if I could eat a whole lot of meals put together and not be uncomfortable afterwards. Now I'm sure your poem doesn't make you feel like that?"

"No, it doesn't," Polly admitted.

"Does it make you feel anything?" the wolf persisted.

"No-o-o. But I like it. I shall have my children born on Sunday and then they'll be like what the poem says."

"That would be nice," agreed the wolf. "But one very seldom gets a Sunday child. I believe they're delicious, even if you eat them without cooking at all!"

"I didn't mean to eat," said Polly coldly. "I meant children of my own. Bonny and blithe and all that."

"What day did you say you were born on," the wolf inquired. "Did you say Monday or Friday?"

"Monday," said Polly; "fair of face."

"Fairly tough," said the wolf thoughtfully to himself. "Still, there's always steaming," he added. "Or stewing in a very slow oven. Worth trying, I think."

He made a bound over the garden wall on to the lawn. But Polly had been too quick for him. She had run into the house and shut the door behind her before the wolf had recovered his balance from landing on the grass.

"Ah well," sighed the wolf, picking himself up. "These literary discussions! Very often don't get one anywhere. A tough proposition, this Polly. I'll concentrate on something tenderer and easier to get for today."

And picking up the daisy chain, which Polly had left behind her, he wound it round his ears and trotted peacefully out of the garden and away down the road.

Catherine Storr

This is a story from the Bible, and it describes something that happened during a war between the Hebrews and the Philistines.

Goliath, the Philistine, was so big and strong that the whole Hebrew army was afraid of him. David, the Hebrew, was young and small. He knew that he would never be as strong as Goliath, even with weapons and armour. So, instead of relying on physical strength he used his speed and lightness. He also had faith in his God, and this gave him the courage he needed to face Goliath.

David and Goliath

Goliath was a giant of a man. He was three metres tall, a real freak. He had a voice to go with his size. "Come on and fight," he bellowed across the valley.

On the other side stood Saul and the Israelites. They listened and they were frightened. They didn't know what to do.

"Come on," shouted Goliath again. "One against one. Who's going to come and fight? Send out your champion. If he can beat me, our army will surrender to you. If I beat him, you surrender to us. Nobody will get killed."

In the Israelite camp nobody moved. Even from this distance Goliath looked enormous. He stood half-way down the opposite hillside. His bronze helmet shone in the sun. It made him look even bigger. He wore armour too on his body and legs. The staff he carried looked like a tree trunk and he had a spear to match.

He must weigh a ton, thought Saul. He could kill a normal man just by sitting on him.

"What's up?" came Goliath's voice again. "Are you scared?"

From the ranks of the Philistines behind Goliath came a sound of distant laughter.

It was no good. If Saul sent a man, he would lose. If he didn't, his men would know he was scared. Saul didn't know what to do.

Behind him Saul heard an argument taking place.

"What's going on?" said a voice Saul knew.

"Where did you come from?" asked another angry voice. "Who's looking after the sheep this time?"

"The sheep are all right. Dad sent me with some things for you. What's going on?"

"Oh, nothing for kids like you. This is man's stuff."

It was David arguing with his elder brother, Eliab. David had been back home on the farm. Eliab and his other brothers were part of Saul's army.

Just at that moment Goliath started shouting again. "Come on," he roared. "Who's going to come and fight?"

David looked around. "Well?" he asked. "Who's going? What's that heathen Philistine got against the armies of God?"

"Oh, shut up, you cocky fool," said Eliab, who had never liked David since he had been chosen to go to Saul. "You've only come to see a fight."

"What have I done now?" said David. "All right," he said. "I'll go and fight him if you won't."

Eliab laughed, but somebody had already told Saul that there was a volunteer.

Saul groaned when he saw who it was. "You can't go," he said to David. "You're only a teenager. Goliath has been a soldier for years."

"So what?" said David. "I've taken on a lion and bears when I've been on my own with the sheep. He looks a bit like a bear," he added, looking across to where Goliath stood.

For the first time Saul and his men smiled.

"All right," said Saul. "Get on with it and God be with you." There was nothing else he could do. "Take my armour," he added. "You will need it."

Willing hands helped David put on Saul's heavy breastplate and helmet. Then the bronze leg-guards were strapped on. A sword was placed in one hand, a spear in the other.

David tried to walk. He couldn't. He stumbled and fell. It took four men to lift him up.

"Take this lot off," gasped David. "If I'm going to fight, I'll fight my way."

Dressed only in a loincloth and carrying a sling, he set off down the hillside to the stream at the bottom.

Goliath saw him coming. He threw back his head and roared with laughter.

"Look at this," he called out. "They've sent out a little scrap for the birds."

David had stopped at the stream. He bent down and chose five round stones. He put four in the bag he always carried round his neck. The other he put in his sling.

Goliath came down the hill. He walked heavily and he was still laughing.

David leapt across the stream and ran towards Goliath. "It's you who's going to be food for the birds," he called. "The power I have is the strength of our God of Israel."

Goliath still came on. David stopped. In his right hand he held his sling. He began to whirl it. Round and round it went, slowly and deliberately. Goliath thumped down the slope towards him.

He was ten metres away when, with a sudden hard twist of his arm, David let go of one of the sling straps. The stone flew out like a bullet.

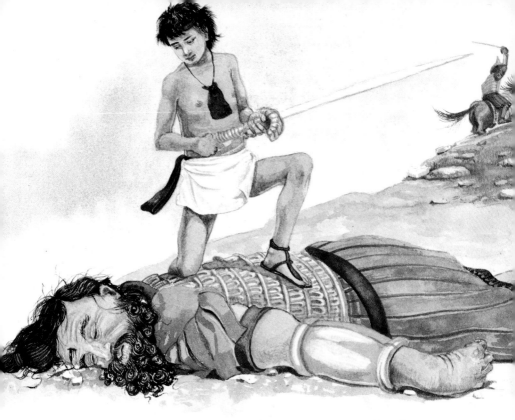

Goliath had no chance. The stone caught him between the eyes. The ground shook as he fell. David moved like lightning. He grabbed Goliath's huge sword. It glinted in the sun as he raised it and then down it came. Goliath's head rolled slowly away from his body.

For a minute there was complete silence in the valley. Then there was a noise of running feet. David looked up. Behind him his own army was running down the hill shouting and cheering. Above him the Philistines were running in the opposite direction.

told by J. G. Priestley

It is usually worth trying to do something difficult, even though we will not always succeed. The Engine in this poem tries very hard to get up a hill. But does the ending surprise you?

The Little Blue Engine

The little blue engine looked up at the hill.
His light was weak, his whistle was shrill.
He was tired and small, and the hill was tall,
And his face blushed red as he softly said,
"I think I can, I think I can, I think I can."

So he started up with a chug and a strain,
And he puffed and pulled with might and main.
And slowly he climbed, a foot at a time,
And his engine coughed as he whispered soft,
"I think I can, I think I can, I think I can."

With a squeak and a creak and a toot and a sigh,
With an extra hope and an extra try,
He would not stop – now he neared the top –
And strong and proud he cried out loud,
"I think I can, I think I can, I think I can!"

He was almost there, when – *CRASH! SMASH! BASH!*
He slid down and mashed into engine hash
On the rocks below . . . which goes to show
If the track is tough and the hill is rough,
THINKING you can just ain't enough!

Shel Silverstein

Has anyone ever dared you to do something frightening or dangerous? Have you ever taken the dare so that people won't think you are a coward? Why do we behave in a silly way in order to look big?

DID I EVER TELL YOU...
about taking a stupid dare
from a boy called Colin?

On the way home from school there was a whole road of houses which had perfect walls to the front gardens. They were perfect because they were just the right height and if no one was about, you could walk along them. The walls were built like steps at either end which made the walk even more fun. When we weren't playing games jumping over all the cracks in the pavements or going along the kerb one foot on and one foot off, we often balanced along a wall. Most of us were quite

good at it and hardly ever fell off into any garden flowers.

There was just one garden where we didn't walk along the wall and that was the one where the nettles grew right up against the wall. We all knew how painful it would be if the nettles brushed our legs as we walked along the wall.

One day, as we were going home, I did a really stupid thing. I accepted a dare from a boy called Colin to balance along the nettle wall. We had already balanced along three walls following each other one by one. We jumped down when we came to the nettle wall.

"I dare you to walk along that wall," challenged Colin.

"Go on," said my friend Margaret. "I bet you could easily."

I hesitated. It would really sting if I brushed against the nettles.

"Dare you again," said Colin.

So I pulled my socks up really high as far as they would go. I pulled my sleeves right down over my hands. Then I climbed onto the wall. I didn't want Margaret and Colin to think I couldn't take a dare.

I went along the wall very carefully. It was easy. Then a window opened in the nettly house and a voice yelled, "Get down at once, you brat."

I was so surprised I fell down. Sad to say I didn't fall down the road side onto the pavement – I fell into the garden full of nettles and I fell head first. Every bit of me which wasn't covered by clothes was stung with nettles. I ran home as fast as I could. My head, my neck, my face, my fingers and legs from my dress down to my socks turned into one great nettle sting – bright red and very painful.

Our mother ran a warm bath and put some soothing powder into it.

"Keep dipping your head under," she instructed, "until you feel better."

So I sat for a long time in the warm bath until the stinging had nearly stopped and the water was nearly cold.

"You must be almost completely daft to take a dare like that," said my brother Francis when he saw me. "I never go anywhere near nettles."

Just for once Francis seemed right and sensible and grown-up.

But the very next day a strange thing happened. Francis had a race down the hill with Derek on his bike. Francis was determined to win the race so he didn't slow down at the corner. He went so fast he couldn't stop and went head first into a nettle bed.

When Derek brought him home, our mother ran another warm bath and put some soothing powder into it.

"This is a very bad year for children and a very good year for nettles," she said. "I suppose some years are like that!"

After that I didn't take any more dares for anything and Francis didn't try so hard to win bike races.

Iris Grender

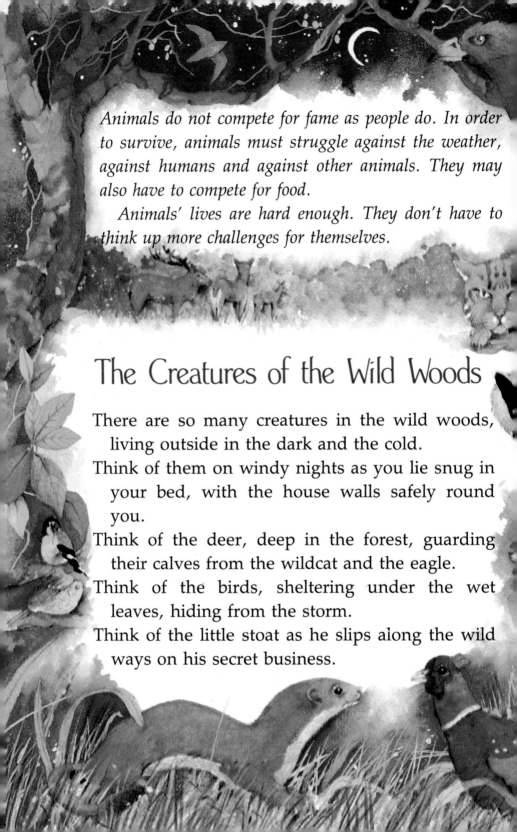

Animals do not compete for fame as people do. In order to survive, animals must struggle against the weather, against humans and against other animals. They may also have to compete for food.

Animals' lives are hard enough. They don't have to think up more challenges for themselves.

The Creatures of the Wild Woods

There are so many creatures in the wild woods, living outside in the dark and the cold.

Think of them on windy nights as you lie snug in your bed, with the house walls safely round you.

Think of the deer, deep in the forest, guarding their calves from the wildcat and the eagle.

Think of the birds, sheltering under the wet leaves, hiding from the storm.

Think of the little stoat as he slips along the wild ways on his secret business.

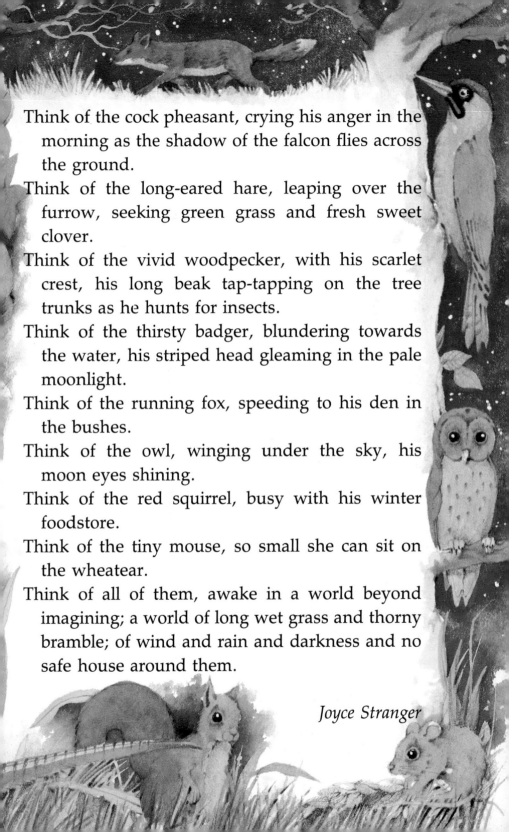

Think of the cock pheasant, crying his anger in the morning as the shadow of the falcon flies across the ground.

Think of the long-eared hare, leaping over the furrow, seeking green grass and fresh sweet clover.

Think of the vivid woodpecker, with his scarlet crest, his long beak tap-tapping on the tree trunks as he hunts for insects.

Think of the thirsty badger, blundering towards the water, his striped head gleaming in the pale moonlight.

Think of the running fox, speeding to his den in the bushes.

Think of the owl, winging under the sky, his moon eyes shining.

Think of the red squirrel, busy with his winter foodstore.

Think of the tiny mouse, so small she can sit on the wheatear.

Think of all of them, awake in a world beyond imagining; a world of long wet grass and thorny bramble; of wind and rain and darkness and no safe house around them.

Joyce Stranger

If we are caring and thoughtful we can help animals and make their lives easier. In this story, Wallace is worried because his cat has been catching birds and mice. What can he do to help?

Helping the Birds

One day when Dad and Wallace and Henry came down for breakfast they found little brown feathers scattered over the kitchen floor.

"Oh, no!" said Wallace. "Wussy's had a bird again, Dad."

"That's the second this week," said Dad. "Do you remember the sparrow he got when the builders were here?"

"Yes," said Wallace, "and he got a mouse once. Let's not give him any breakfast, Dad."

"If we don't he'll only catch more birds and things," Dad replied and he gave Wussy his plate of meat. "Anyway, it's his nature to catch things – like a lion catching a zebra."

That very same day Wallace came out of the front door and there was Wussy with a little bird in his mouth. Wallace shouted and stamped at

Wussy and he ran away. The little bird stayed where it was, cowering on the doorstep.

"Naughty Wussy," said Wallace. "Is it hurt, Dad?"

"Doesn't seem to be," Dad replied. But the little bird just sat there with its bright startled eyes.

"Shall we look after it, Dad?" said Wallace.

"If we don't Wussy will only get it again, or it'll die of cold." And Dad picked up the little bird in his hands.

"Is it a sparrow?" asked Wallace.

"No, I think it's a robin."

Then they got a cardboard box and Wallace put some twigs and fluffy dried grass in it for a nest. They brought a little ash-tray for water and they gave it some peanuts, a cheese biscuit, the remains of Henry's apple, half a Weetabix and some bread. They also dug up two worms, a big one and a little one.

"Well, he's bound to like *something* there," said Dad. They watched to see what the bird would do but it wouldn't do anything. It had hopped into a corner and there it sat. They could see its body moving up and down with the beating of its heart.

"He's had a bad shock," said Dad. "Let's leave him be."

They put wire-netting over the top to keep Wussy out.

At bed-time Wallace looked in again but the little bird still hadn't moved.

"Wussy didn't hurt him badly, did he?" Wallace asked.

"We'll see in the morning," said Dad.

But in the morning the bird was dead, lying on the bottom of the box beside his water-tray. They buried him under Wallace's apple tree.

At breakfast they could see Wussy crouching at his special pouncing place on the other side of the lawn.

"Wussy's catching more mice, Dad," said Wallace. "I think we should get rid of him."

"Well," said Dad, "if we didn't have Wussy we'd have mice doing droppings under the sink and eating the bottom out of the porridge oats sack. He does a good job for us."

"But he needn't catch birds too," said Wallace. "*They* don't do any harm."

"They do to my vegetables," said Dad, "but I suppose as it's winter there are no vegetables for them to eat."

"Let's put some food out for them, Dad," said Wallace. "They can have my bread." And he threw it out of the back door.

"Wussy will pounce on them if they come close to the house," said Dad. "We'll just have to build a bird table – that's all."

So they found a bit of sawn-off branch for a post, rather bent but long. "It must be high, you see," said Dad. "Otherwise Wussy will jump up to it."

They thumped the post into the ground in the middle of the lawn. "Now the top," said Dad.

Mum had put some strips of pork fat on a string so they hung that off one corner of the table and put some breadcrumbs on top.

Then they went inside to watch. In no time at all a pair of blue tits came and hung upside down on the fat to peck at it.

"Oh! Dad, look!" Wallace cried out. "Here comes Wussy. He'll catch them!"

But the birds flew away long before Wussy got near them. "They can see him coming across the lawn," said Dad. "And anyway they're so high up Wussy can't reach them."

They watched Wussy jumping up on his hind legs to bat at the string of fat spinning in the air. But he couldn't reach it.

"Ha! ha!" said Wallace. "That's fixed him, Dad."

Wussy wandered slowly away and the birds came back.

The next morning at breakfast they watched the blue tits on the fat and the sparrows and starlings fighting over the bread.

"Wussy can't get them, can he, Dad?" said Wallace. "I wonder where he is." Then he saw him. He was crouched at his pouncing place, very still except for his tail which was swishing from side to side.

"Oh dear!" said Wallace. "Wussy can still catch the mice, can't he, Dad?"

"Yes, I'm afraid he can, and he will," said Dad. "But we have done something for the birds, Wallace, and we can't save everything."

Simon Watson

The earth provides life for all plants and creatures. They take what they need from the earth but never destroy its power to give life.

Only humans take too much from the earth. People need houses to live in and so they drive away animals to build roads and houses. Farmers need big fields to grow crops and so they destroy plants and trees to make space.

Here is the story of one piece of land and all the demands made of it. Who do you think has most right to use the land – plants, animals or humans? Or can they all live together?

Herons' Field

Herons' Field was flat and grassy. It stretched from a clump of oak-trees at one end to a pebbly stream at the other. It was called Herons' Field because of the herons which used to hunt for sticklebacks in the stream.

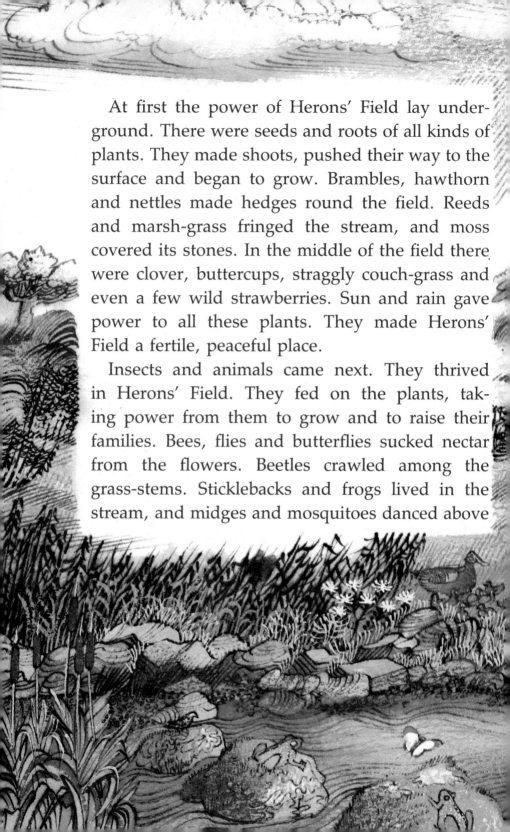

At first the power of Herons' Field lay underground. There were seeds and roots of all kinds of plants. They made shoots, pushed their way to the surface and began to grow. Brambles, hawthorn and nettles made hedges round the field. Reeds and marsh-grass fringed the stream, and moss covered its stones. In the middle of the field there were clover, buttercups, straggly couch-grass and even a few wild strawberries. Sun and rain gave power to all these plants. They made Herons' Field a fertile, peaceful place.

Insects and animals came next. They thrived in Herons' Field. They fed on the plants, taking power from them to grow and to raise their families. Bees, flies and butterflies sucked nectar from the flowers. Beetles crawled among the grass-stems. Sticklebacks and frogs lived in the stream, and midges and mosquitoes danced above it. There were rabbit-burrows in the oak-copse, and voles, shrews and fieldmice darted through the undergrowth and nibbled the seeds and stalks. Predators lived there too. Their power and life came from the creatures they fed on. There were spiders, an owl, a family of weasels, a fox, even a peregrine circling overhead.

The first changes came when Country Farms Limited bought Herons' Field. They were dairy farmers. They were interested in letting their cows turn the power of grass and clover into milk. They put their cattle into Herons' Field to graze. They cut down the hedgerows and put electric fences up. They trimmed the oak-trees and scythed the undergrowth. They were business people, powerful and efficient. All the rabbits, mice and weasels, even the fox and the falcon, were afraid of them, and moved away.

After a while, men with measuring-tapes and poles came to Herons' Field. They were surveyors, and their job was to measure the land and make a map of it. They worked for a fuel company. The company was not interested in the power of plants, but in another kind of underground power: oil. They bought Herons' Field from the dairy farmers, and began to drill. The air was filled with the racket of machines.

The fuel company found no oil under Herons' Field. They drilled for a year, and then took their men and machinery somewhere else. The field was left empty. At first its soil was torn and broken, as if the ground had been wounded in a fight. But underground, the roots and seeds had not been killed. They soon showed their power again, and plants began to grow. Insects, birds and animals moved back. The Field's life went on as if it had never been disturbed. A family of gypsies moved in, with a lorry, a caravan and two old horses. They let their horses graze on the grass, and parked their caravan beside the stream.

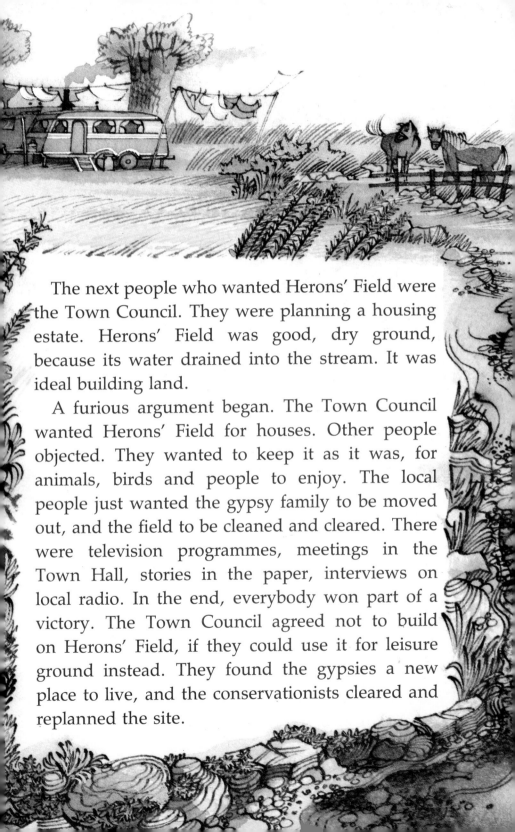

The next people who wanted Herons' Field were the Town Council. They were planning a housing estate. Herons' Field was good, dry ground, because its water drained into the stream. It was ideal building land.

A furious argument began. The Town Council wanted Herons' Field for houses. Other people objected. They wanted to keep it as it was, for animals, birds and people to enjoy. The local people just wanted the gypsy family to be moved out, and the field to be cleaned and cleared. There were television programmes, meetings in the Town Hall, stories in the paper, interviews on local radio. In the end, everybody won part of a victory. The Town Council agreed not to build on Herons' Field, if they could use it for leisure ground instead. They found the gypsies a new place to live, and the conservationists cleared and replanned the site.

What happened to Herons' Field in the end? If you want to visit it now, you have to go down the road out of town, past the neat houses of the Heronsfield Estate. At the edge of the estate is a school, and the school has a large, grassy playing-field. It stretches from a single oak-tree at the edge of the playground, all the way to a stream at the other end. There are wire-mesh fences at each side, but honeysuckle and blackberries grow along them, and poke bright flowers and berries through the mesh. Among the smooth grass of the field, if you search carefully, you'll find clover-plants, buttercups and even a few wild strawberries. Local people say that rabbits come out at night to feed, and that the whole place is alive with fieldmice, shrews and voles. One person even claims to have seen a fox.

Over the years, all kinds of people have used Herons' Field, and changed the way it looks. But in all that time it has never once lost its basic power: the power of life.

Kenneth McLeish

Marie Curie was very clever, but at the time she lived people thought that women should not study at University, nor have anything to do with science. What do you think they were supposed to do?

Marie Curie had to compete against these ideas about women. She also had to work hard at the task she had set herself.

Against the Odds

The schoolchildren were talking about what they wanted to be when they grew up. "A priest," said one boy. "A lawyer," said another. "A writer," said another.

"I want to be a scientist," said Maria.

All the boys laughed. "How can you be a scientist?" they said. "You're a girl. Girls have babies and look after families. They don't go out to work."

Maria said nothing. She knew it would be hard. In Poland, where she lived a century ago, girls were not even allowed to learn science at school. "It's a boys' subject," people said. "It's not for girls."

But Maria had a plan. Instead of learning science, she learned languages at school. She was good at French. Then, as soon as she was old enough, she went to live in France. She studied science at university there. French people thought it strange that a girl should want to study science. But no one stopped her.

It was hard for Maria to learn science. All the teaching was in French, and was about things she had never heard of. She woke up at five each morning, and worked for three hours before breakfast. She stayed at the university until ten each night, and then worked at home on her books until two or three o'clock. She had little time for sleep.

If Maria had not had courage, she would soon have given up. She was like an athlete, training and training to win a race. She was training her mind, not her muscles. Her race was to be a better scientist than anyone else. She had no women to beat, because no women learned science. Her race was against men, and she had to prove that she was the best scientist in France.

In 1893, when Maria was 26, she won the first part of her race. After only two years' studying, she came top in the exams. She was the best scientist of her age in France. She began working with a young man called Pierre Curie. They fell in love, and two years later they married. Maria changed her name to Marie, in French style.

Marie and Pierre Curie were fascinated by radio-activity. Nowadays people think this an important thing to study. But ninety years ago it was practically unknown. People thought that Marie and Pierre were wasting their time. "No real scientist bothers with that," they said. "Why don't you do something useful instead?"

But Marie and Pierre insisted. They were determined. They had no money to finance their work. So Pierre taught in the university every day, and Marie taught science in a girls' school. Every evening, and every morning before teaching began, they worked on their experiments. They had no

proper room to work in. A hut in the university gardens was their laboratory. They used fire, boiling water and acid to purify black grains of metal ore, called pitchblende. They were looking for a new metal, never seen before. To find it, they had to purify tonne after tonne of ore.

The work took years. The air was full of oily smoke. The acid burned their hands and stained their clothes. It was filthy, endless labour. It was hardest of all for Marie. For part of the time she was pregnant, and the fumes made her sick. But she would not give in. She insisted on sharing the work equally with Pierre. She was determined to succeed.

In 1902, after four years' work, Marie and Pierre discovered the new metal they had been looking for. They called it radium. Out of eight tonnes of ore, they ended up with one gram of radium. It was like a handful of rough grey salt. It was a triumph. People thought radium miraculous. They used its rays to cure disease. Even today, radio-therapy (as it is called) is a way of helping people with cancer. The radio-active rays kill the cancer-cells.

Discovering radium made the Curies famous. In 1904 they won the Nobel Prize for physics, one of the world's highest honours. Pierre was made a university professor. Their struggle seemed to be over. Then, in 1906, there was a traffic accident and Pierre was killed. Marie was a widow, with two young children to bring up.

Once again, Marie's determination helped her. She asked to be made professor in Pierre's place. She argued and argued till she got the job. She went on working with radium, and in 1911 won a second Nobel Prize. In 1919 she went back to Poland, and became a professor at Warsaw University. She was the first woman professor in Poland, and when she died in 1934, aged 67, she was one of the greatest scientists her country had ever known.

All her life, Marie Curie refused to take "no" for an answer. Everything she did was hard. She had to fight to get a job at all. She had to fight to be a scientist. She had to fight to study radio-activity. She had to fight to become a professor. Each time she fought, she won. She loved science, and refused to give up just because things were hard. When she began her life, no one believed that women could do scientific work as well as men. Her success helped to prove them wrong.

Kenneth McLeish

Perhaps the best way to succeed is to help each other. We may gain more if we do not compete against each other.

The Runners

We're hopeless at racing,
Me and my friend.
I'm slow at the start
She's slow at the end.

She has the stitch,
I get sore feet.
And neither one of us
Cares to compete.

But co-operation's
A different case.
You should see us
In the three-legged race!

Alan Ahlberg